# I'M GETTING A BONUS DAD

BY LINDSEY COKER

ILLUSTRATED BY APPLE VERT

Leo had always had a Mom and Dad
Since the day he was born.
But now he had a second Dad
He couldn't help but feel torn.

When he was a little boy,

They would hang out as a trio.

Mom and Dad would take him out

And they would always spoil little Leo.

They would go and play in the park,

They would stop for ice-cream,

They would play catch in the garden,

They would watch films on the big screen.

Mom and Dad and Leo -

The perfect three-person team.

Like three amazing superheroes

Straight from one of Leo's dreams.

But when Leo was six years old,

Things changed in his world forever.

Mom and Dad got a divorce -

They were no longer together.

Now it felt like the team was broken,

There was Mom and there was Dad.

They once came as a package deal -

And that made Leo sad.

But he grew used to the situation.

He still spent lots of time with both.

There were still fine times to be shared

And lots of love and growth.

They were still the three superheroes
With Leo acting as the glue.
Mom and Dad would always be linked
"Because we will always love you!"

Leo was lucky to have two such loving parents.
But things changed again when he was seven -
Mom brought home a brand-new boyfriend,
Ruining Leo's perfect superhero Heaven.

Mom spent more and more time with Greg,

Until one day he got down on one knee.

Mom agreed to marry him

Leo said: "But what about me?!"

Leo didn't want a new Dad -

He loved the one he already had.

He didn't want a new superhero,

The very idea just made him mad.

However, it was Dad who changed his mind

The next time they went to play on a whim.

Dad said: "He's not here to replace me."

"Think of him like your bonus dad, that's him!"

Leo thought about this for a second.

A bonus dad sounded like a treat:

Another parent to love him

That could be rather sweet!

Four heads were definitely better than three
When it came to a superhero squad.
Much more fun to be had and crime to fight
Even if at first it had sounded rather odd.

A Mom, a Dad, and a bonus Dad!

Three parents and three sources love.

This new routine was rather brilliant

And it fit Leo like a glove.

They would still go and play in the park,

They would still stop for ice-cream,

They would still play catch in the garden,

They would still watch films on the big screen!

Only now Leo had another person,

A third parent he'd never had.

Another person to teach and adore him

His very own bonus dad!

Made in the USA
Las Vegas, NV
27 August 2023

76702083R00024